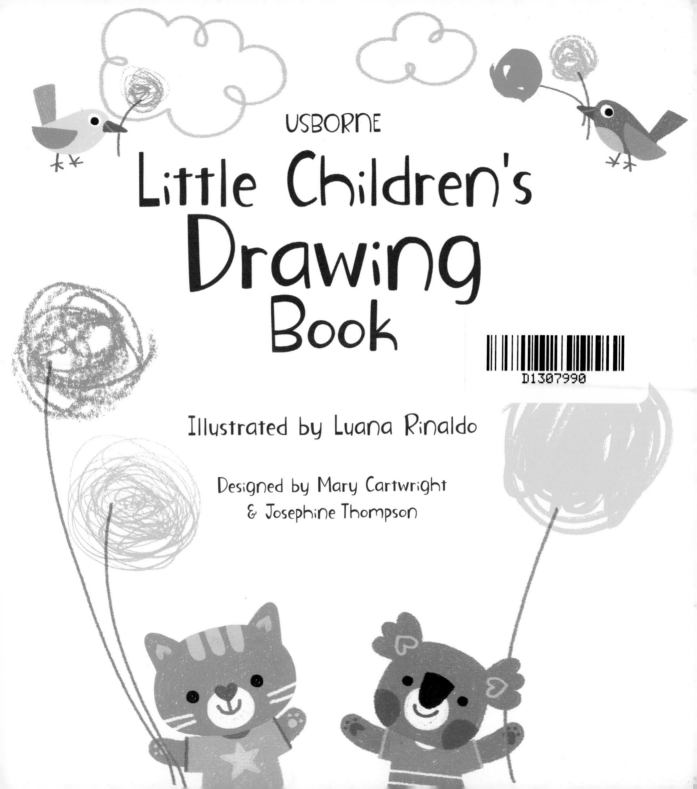

USBORNE

Little Children's Drawing Book

Illustrated by Luana Rinaldo

Designed by Mary Cartwright
& Josephine Thompson

D1307990

Draw long lines to make it rain.

Please draw circles around the socks.

We all need wheels! Please draw some for us.

Bees need flowers.

Draw flowers on all the stems.

What colors will you choose?

We need more lily pads so we can hop around!

I'm a hip, hoppy frog.

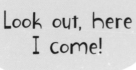
Look out, here I come!

Splash!

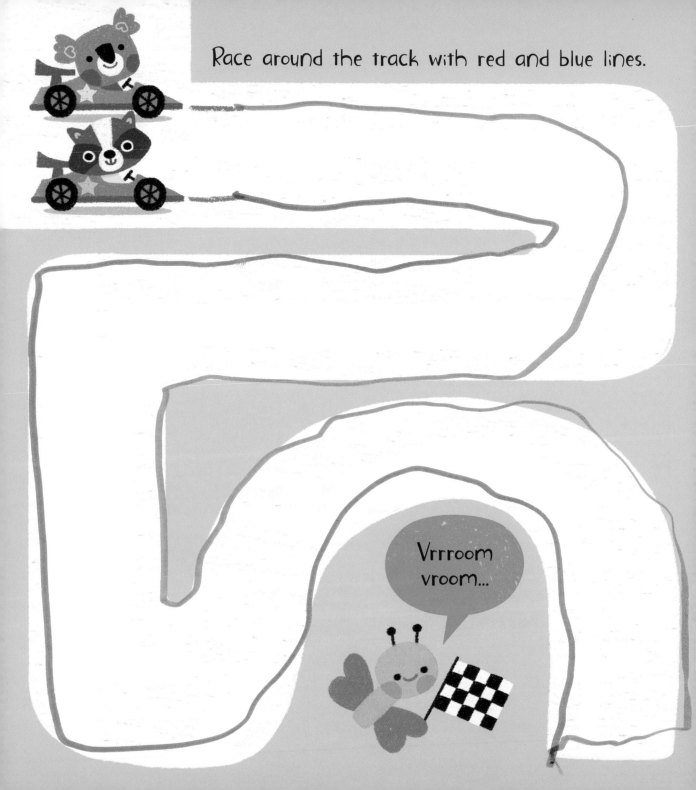

Race around the track with red and blue lines.

Help me draw circles around these bugs.

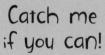
Catch me if you can!

That's not a bug!

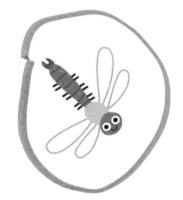

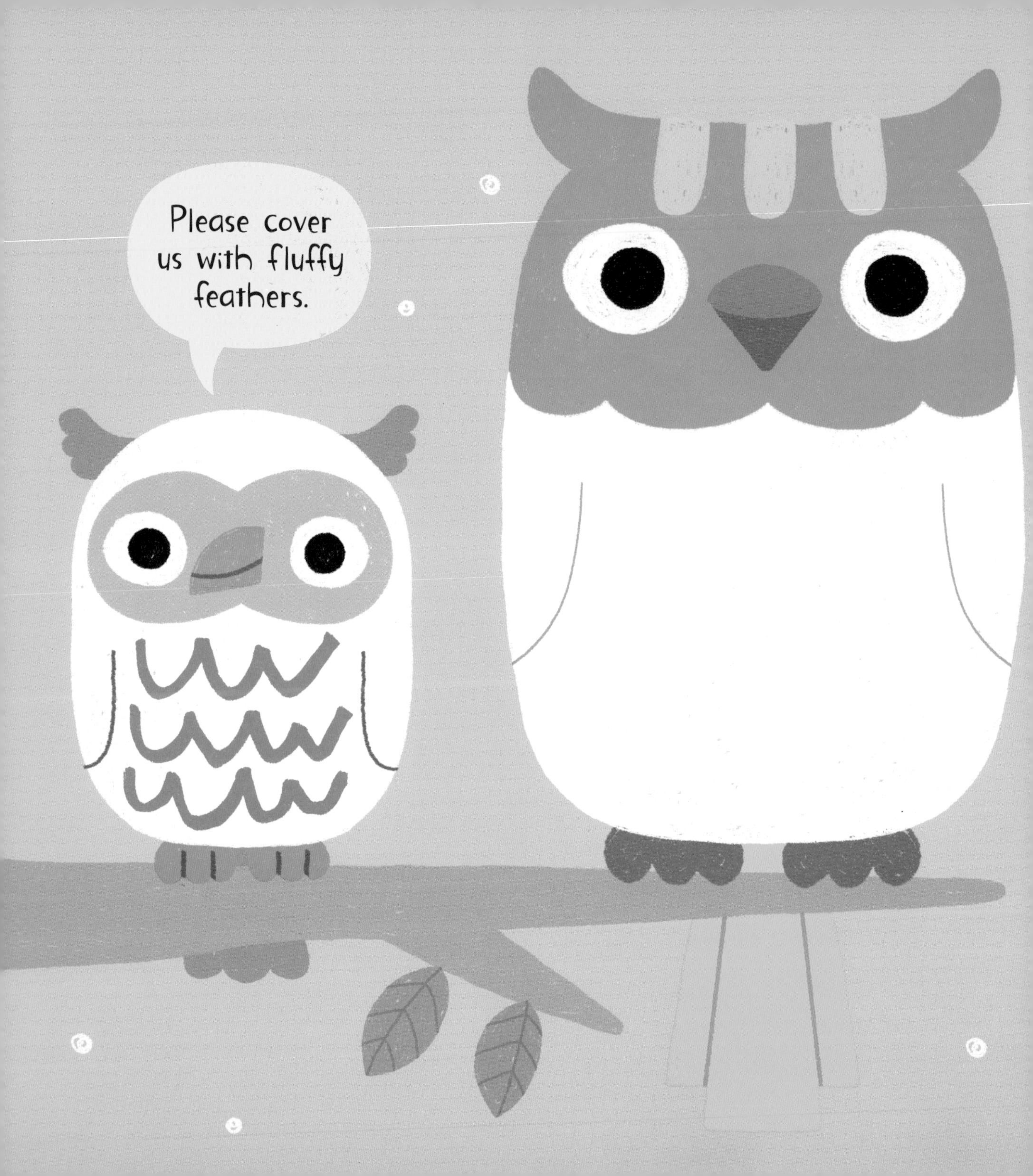
Please cover us with fluffy feathers.

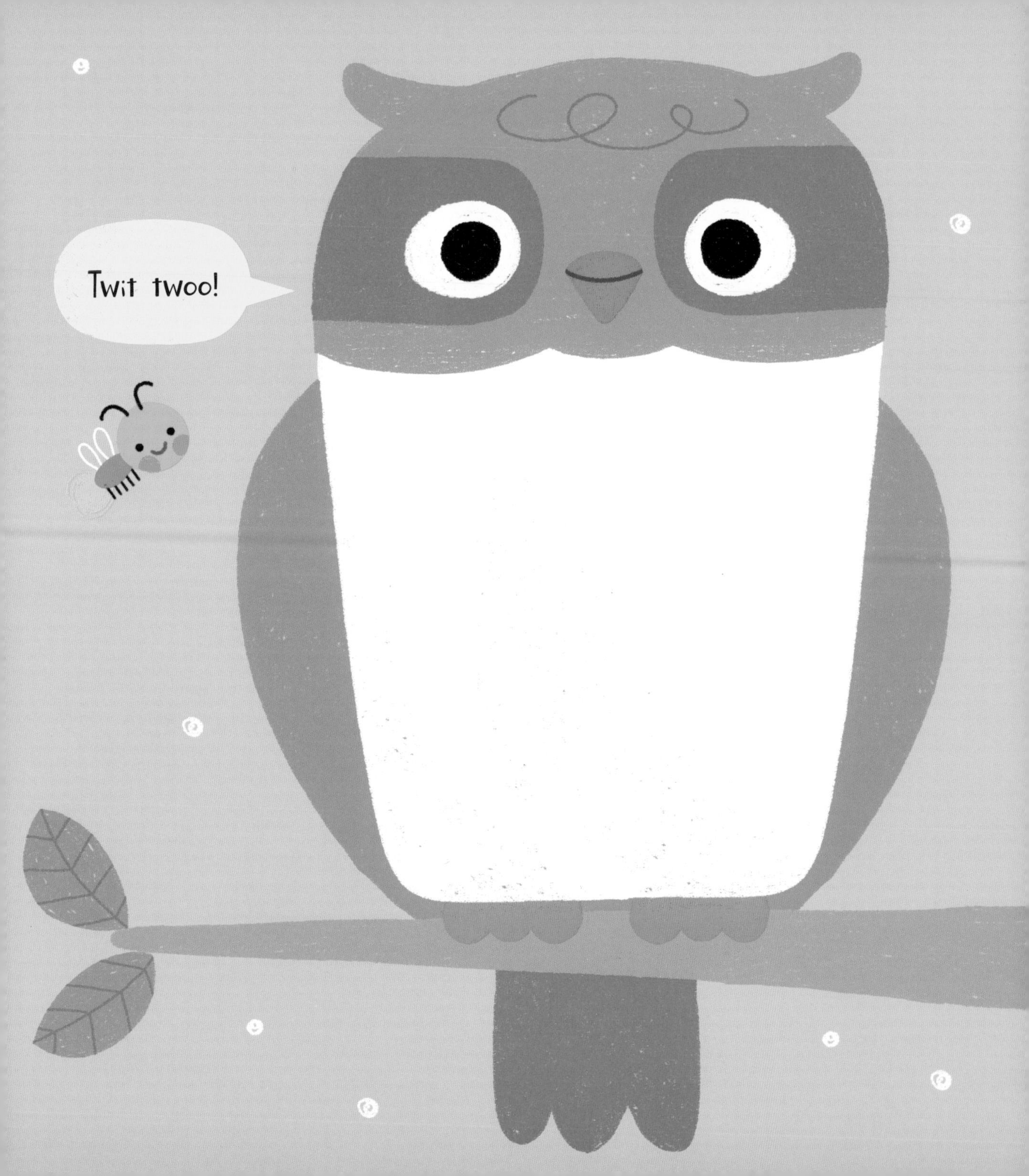
Twit twoo!

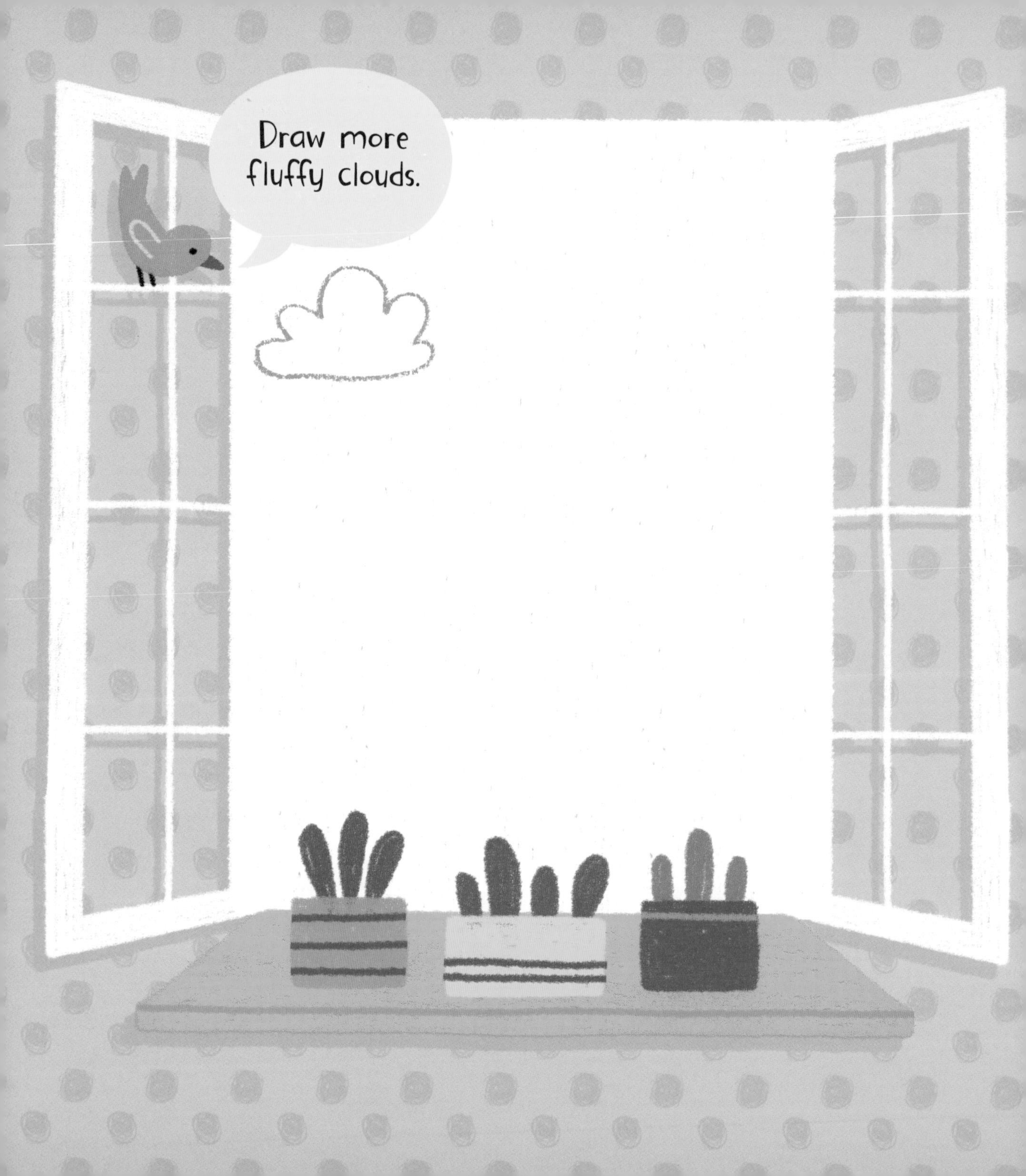
Draw more fluffy clouds.

Notes for grown-ups

The drawing activities in this book encourage young children to try out all sorts of different marks, giving them lots of practice holding and manipulating a pen or pencil. This helps them develop the pen control skills that are essential for learning to write and draw.

straight lines

fat lines and thin lines

wiggly lines

loops and squiggles

Help children get started by giving them bright wax crayons, pencils or washable felt-tip pens of varying thicknesses, suitable for small hands.

Let children experiment with the drawing tools, trying out different marks as they respond to the lively pictures on each page.

dots, circles and swirls

See you again soon!

Edited by Jenny Tyler

With thanks to young helpers Maya, Natalia, Theo, Ruby, Arran, Liam, Abigail, Edward, Elon and Harry for testing activities.